Large-style Activity Book!

Based on the Large Family by Jill Murphy

First published 2008 by Walker Books Ltd
87 Vauxhall Walk, London SE11 5HJ

2 4 6 8 10 9 7 5 3 1

Printed in China

British Library Cataloguing in Publication Data: a catalogue record for this book
is available from the British Library

ISBN 978-1-4063-1325-3

www.walkerbooks.co.uk

WALKER BOOKS
AND SUBSIDIARIES

LONDON • BOSTON • SYDNEY • AUCKLAND

The Large family

Meet Mr and Mrs Large and their children Lester, Laura,
Luke and baby Lucy. Can you trace over their names?

Now it's time for some Large family fun!

Shadow match

Draw lines to match the members of the family to their shadows.

Lester   Lucy   Laura   Mr Large   Luke   Mrs Large

Bake a cake

Laura wants to bake a strawberry sponge cake. The things she will need are shown below. Which trail includes them all?

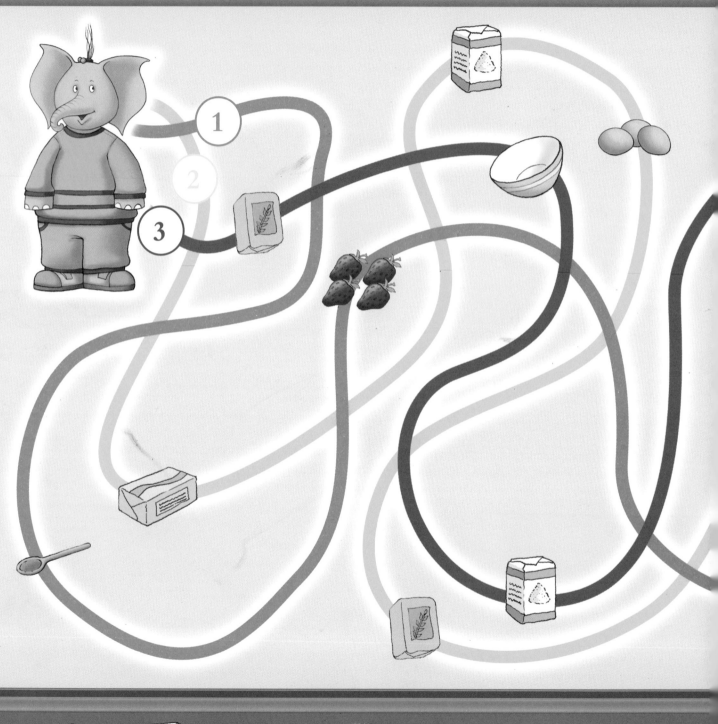

 Butter   Sugar   Eggs   Flour   Strawberries   Bowl   Spoon

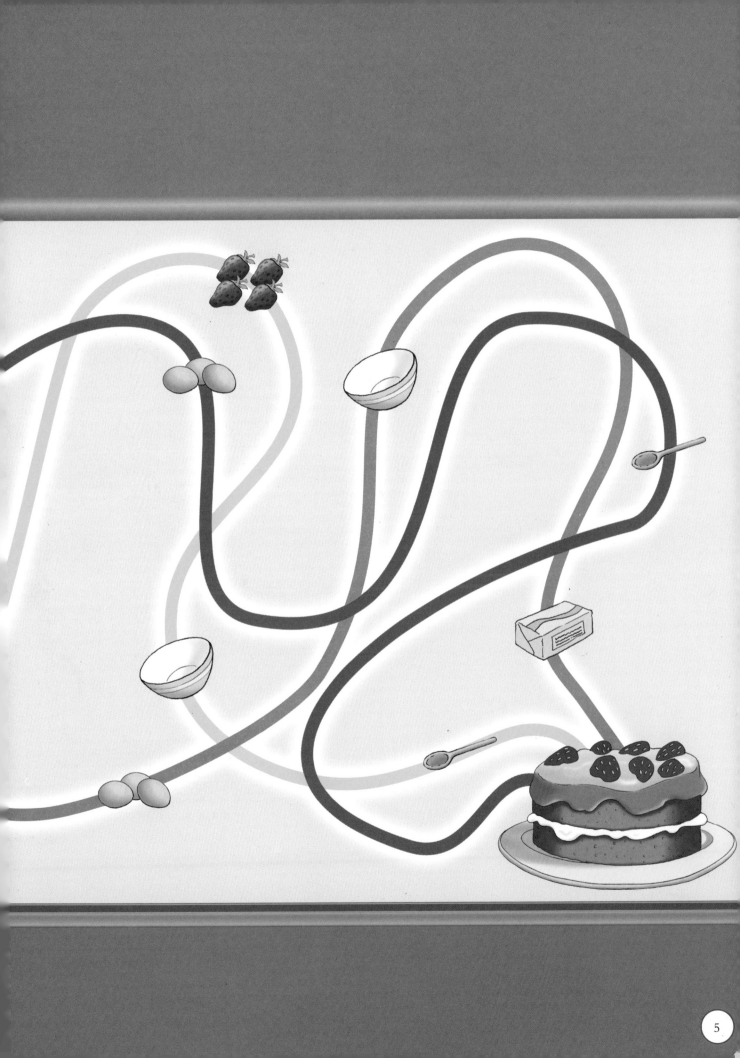

Shopping list

Mrs Large and Lucy are doing their shopping. Tick off the things on their shopping list that are already in the trolley.

Apples ☐   Eggs ☐   Butter ☐   Crisps ☐

Sugar ☐   Flour ☐   Cereal ☐   Milk ☐

What do they still need to find? ....

Trace and colour

Trace over the grey lines, then colour this picture of
Lester with his old friend, Mr Croccy.

Find the pair

Two of these pictures of Laura are exactly the same.
Can you find the matching pair?

How many?

Look at this picture and answer the questions below.
Write the numbers in the boxes.

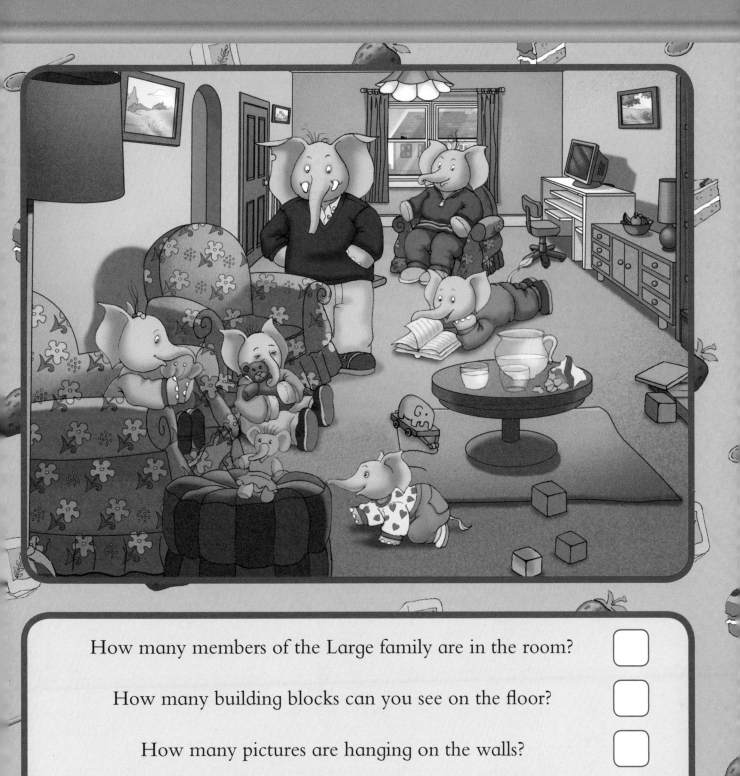

How many members of the Large family are in the room?

How many building blocks can you see on the floor?

How many pictures are hanging on the walls?

How many green armchairs can you see in the room?

Trunk trail

Lester has lost his skateboard and Luke knows where it is. Follow his trunk as he points the way.

Start

Decorate the cake

Help Laura to decorate her cake by drawing some strawberries and coloured sprinkles on the top.

11

Right or wrong?

Have a look at the sentences below these pictures. Put a tick in the box if they are right and a cross if they are wrong.

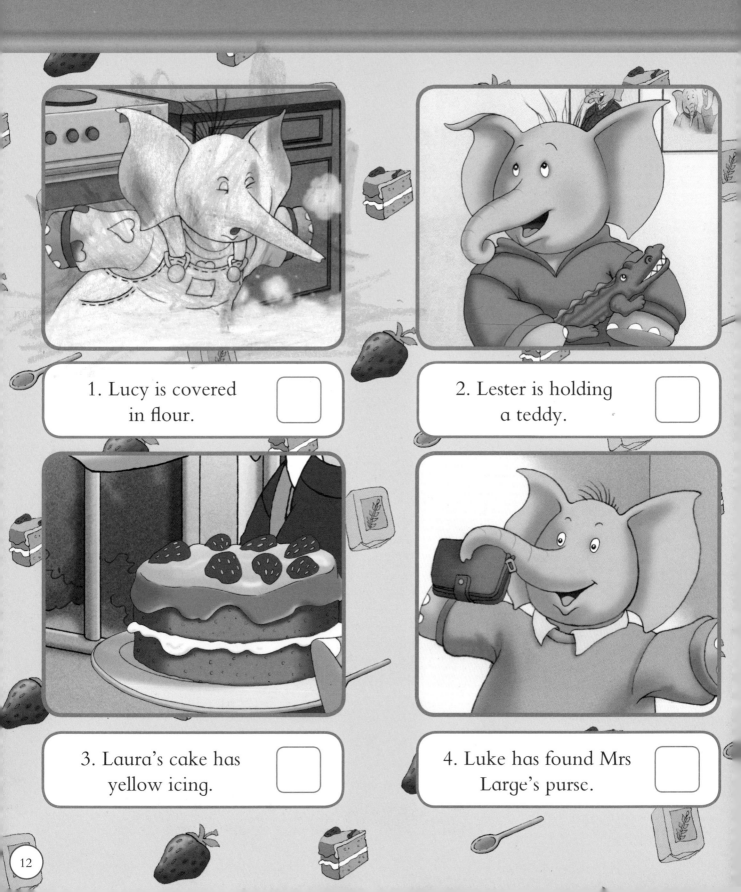

1. Lucy is covered in flour.

2. Lester is holding a teddy.

3. Laura's cake has yellow icing.

4. Luke has found Mrs Large's purse.

5. Luke is playing
with his teddy.

6. Mr Large is
very cross.

7. Lucy is sitting
on a chair.

8. Lester is dressed
as a popstar.

Name the colour

What colour are the things shown below?
Write your answers under the pictures.

1

2

3

4

5

6

Spot the difference

There are six differences between these two pictures of the children on their way to school. Can you spot them all?

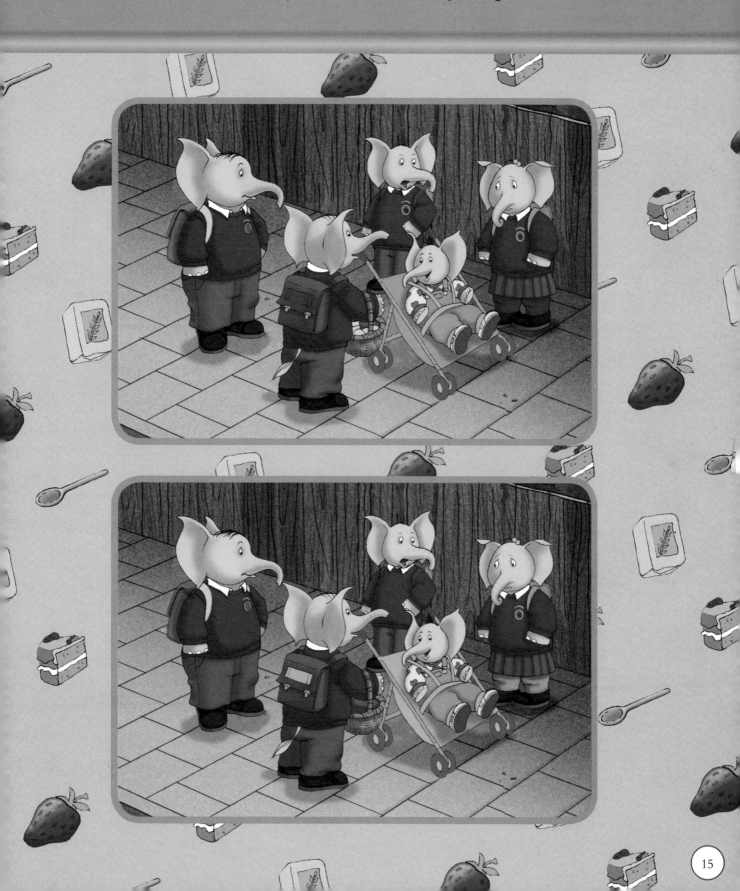

Family photos

Only one of these pictures includes all six members of the Large family.
Which one is it? Who is missing from each of the others?

Spot the shapes

Look carefully at this picture of Lester in the kitchen and see if you can spot the shapes shown at the bottom of the page.

A square

A rectangle

Squares and rectangles have four corners.

Two triangles

Triangles have three corners.

An oval

A circle

Ovals and circles have no corners at all.

Who's who?

Here are some close-up pictures of the Large children. Can you work out who's who and write their names underneath?

L _ _ _ _

L _ _ _ _ _ _

L _ _ _

L _ _ _

Favourite foods

Laura's strawberry jam sponge is a big hit with the Large family. Draw some of your favourite foods, then colour your pictures.

Off to school

Lester is walking to school by himself for the first time.
Can you help him find the way?

Family foursome

The four Large children shown in the top left-hand corner appear again in the same order only once. Can you find them?

Fancy dress fun

There's a fancy dress party at the children's school.
Can you spot the characters listed on the opposite page?

23

Colour by numbers

Colour this picture of Lester using the numbers as a guide.

1 =

2 =

3 =

4 =

5 =

Spot the difference

These pictures look the same, but six
things are different. Can you spot them?

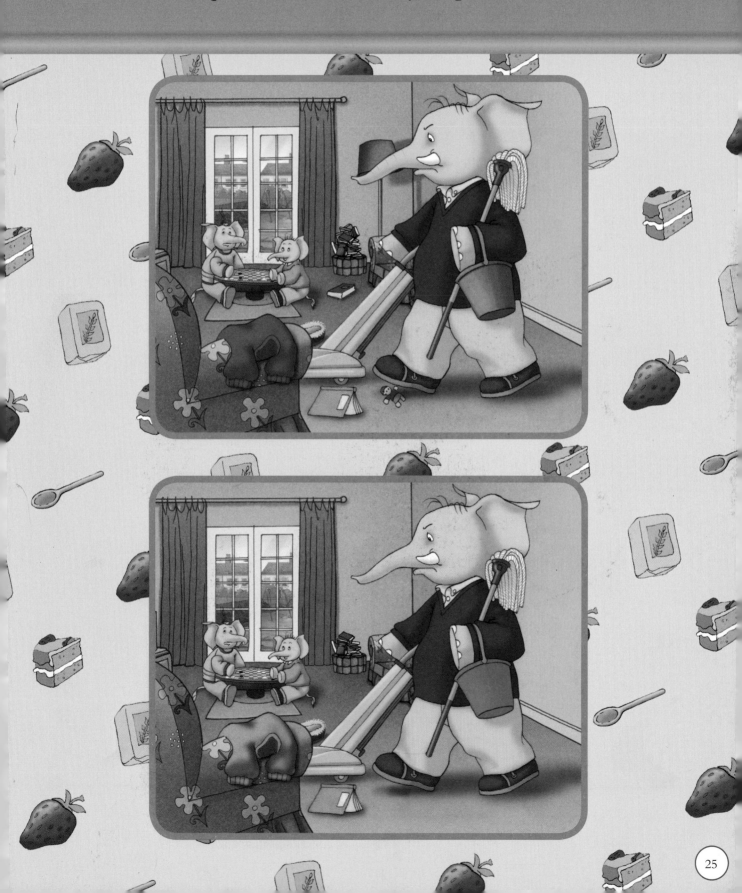

Something beginning with S

Which of the objects below begin with the letter S?
Draw a circle around each one.

Dot-to-dot

Join the dots to complete this picture of Lucy,
then colour it in.

Right or wrong?

Have a look at the sentences below these pictures. Put a tick in the box if they are right and a cross if they are wrong.

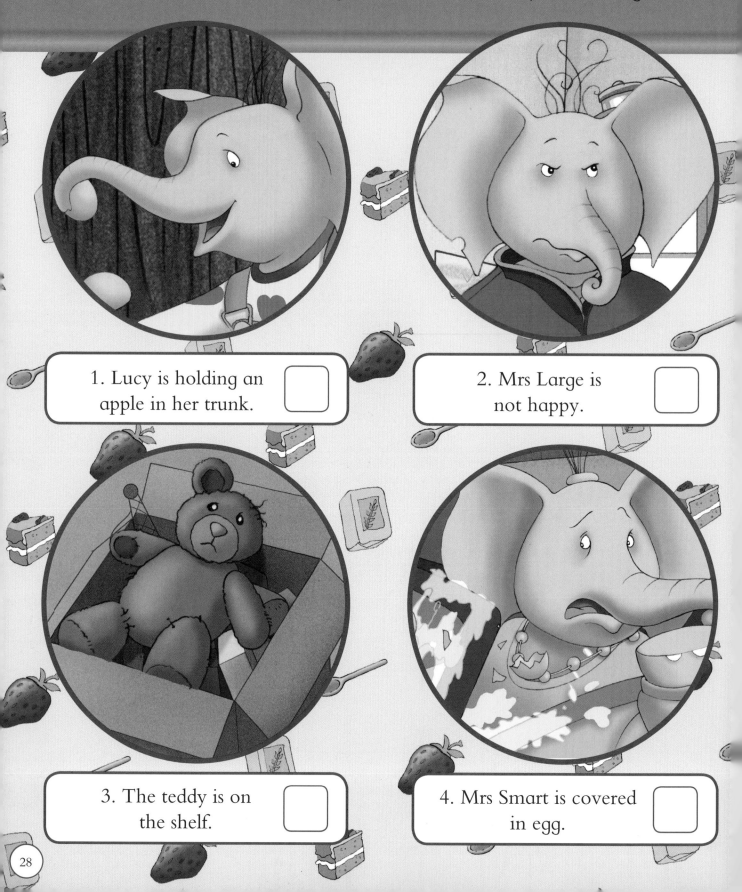

1. Lucy is holding an apple in her trunk.

2. Mrs Large is not happy.

3. The teddy is on the shelf.

4. Mrs Smart is covered in egg.

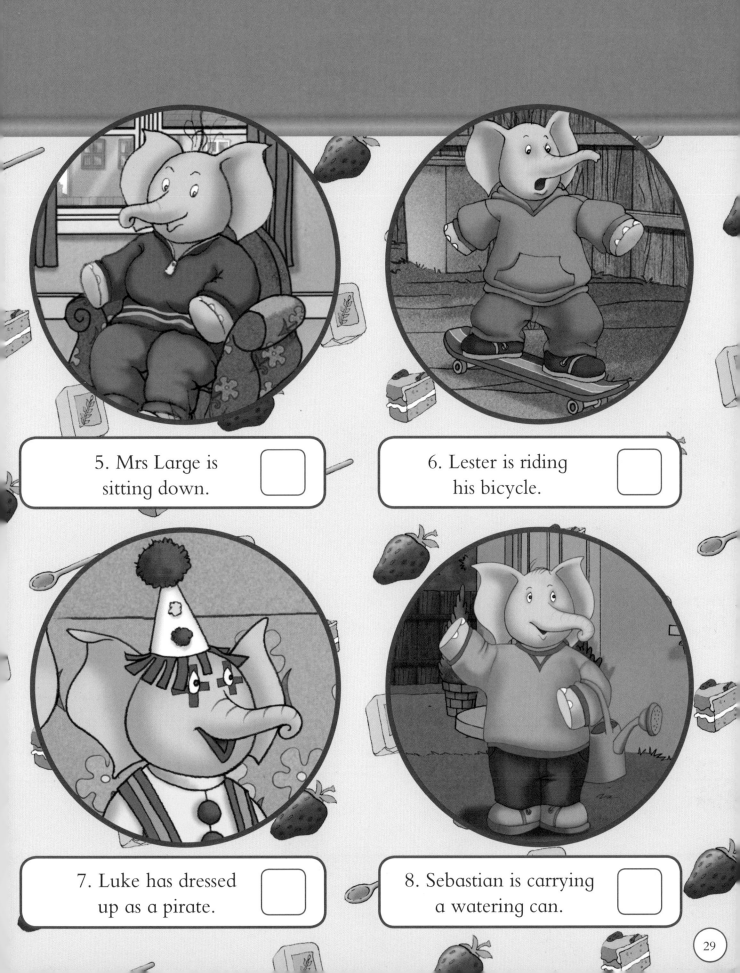

5. Mrs Large is
   sitting down.

6. Lester is riding
   his bicycle.

7. Luke has dressed
   up as a pirate.

8. Sebastian is carrying
   a watering can.

Odd one out

One of these pictures is different to the other three.
Can you spot the odd one out?

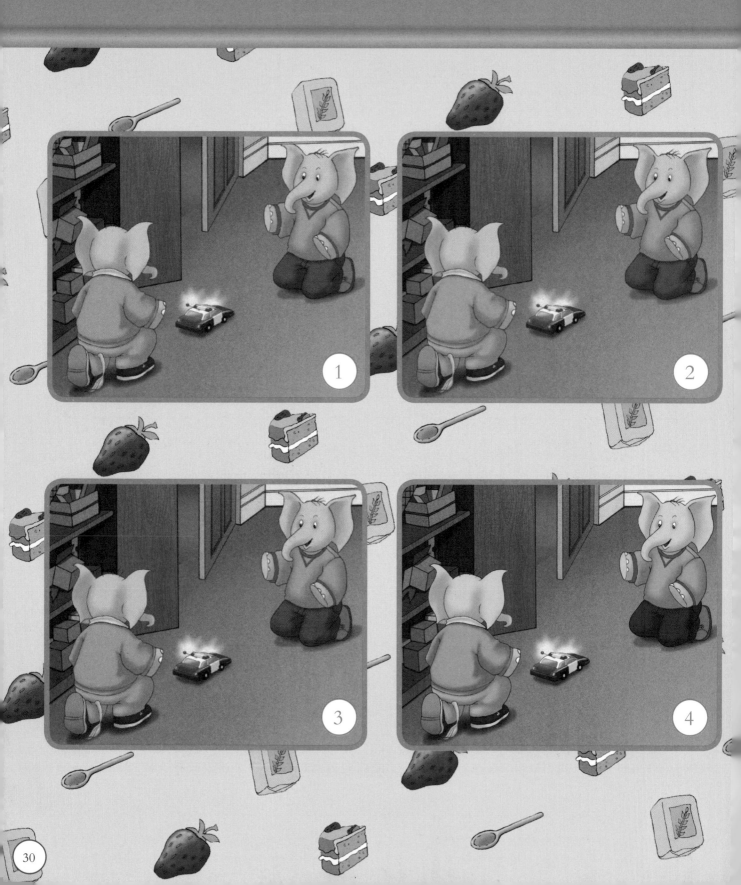

30

Can you find...?

Can you spot the things shown below in this picture of the boys' bedroom? Tick the boxes as you find them.

An aeroplane ☐   A footballer ☐   Two paint pots ☐

A toy car ☐   A CD player ☐   A ball ☐

Answers

Pages 4-5: 2 includes everything Laura needs.

Page 6: they still need to find the apples.

Page 8: the two matching pictures of Laura are 2 and 3.

Page 9: there are six members of the Large family, four building blocks, three pictures and three armchairs.

Page 10

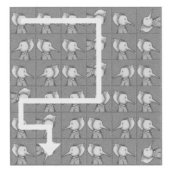

Pages 12-13: sentences 1,4, 6 and 8 are right; sentences 2, 3, 5 and 7 are wrong.

Page 14: 1 red, 2 green, 3 purple, 4 brown, 5 pink, 6 blue

Page 15

Page 16: picture 3 shows all the family; Mrs Large is missing from picture 1; Lester and Lucy are missing from picture 2; Mr Large is missing from picture 4.

Page 17

Page 18: Laura, Lester, Luke, Lucy

Page 20

Page 21

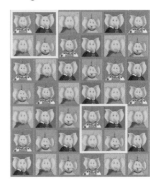

Pages 22-23

Page 25

Page 26: strawberry, sweet, skateboard, spoon

Pages 28-29: sentences 2,4, 5 and 8 are right; sentences 1, 3, 6 and 7 are wrong.

Page 30: 4 is the odd one out.

Page 31